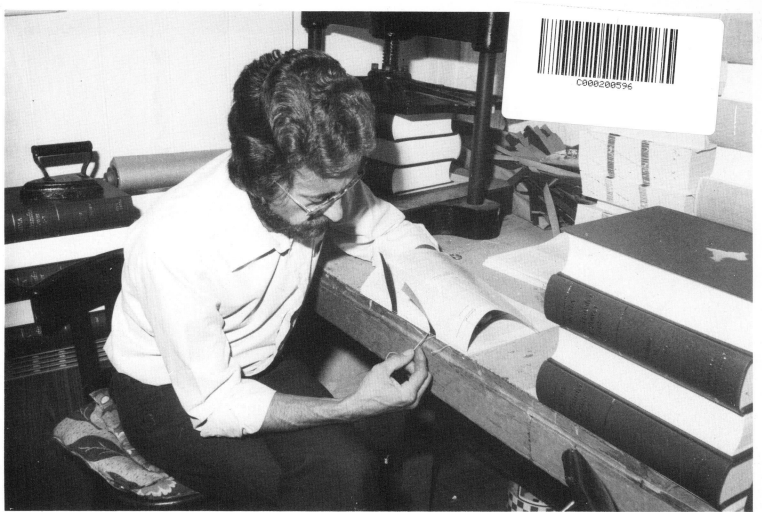

Sewing is perhaps the most important operation in book binding. Pure linen cord is used and offcuts of the binding material for the tapes. A hitch knot known as a kettle stitch is used at the end of each section to join one section to another.

Gluing down the end papers in cloth work is known as 'casing in'. Note the glue pot on the gas ring in the foreground. The inner pot holds the glue and the outer pot hot water.

THE BOOKBINDER

The skill of bookbinding is a craft of some antiquity. A certain Richard at Canterbury in 1508 was binding books for Christchurch Library but the skill dates back far earlier, for monks in England by the XIth Century were producing highly decorative deerskin covers and were reputed to be the finest craftsmen in leather in Europe.

Many other trades are required before a book can be finally assembled, paper-makers, ink-makers, textile workers and tanners for covering material, typefounders, printers, engravers, etc., etc.

Today most books are bound entirely by machines, for bookbinding has been an increasingly mechanised industry for 100 years. There are several first class hand book-binders in Kent working from home, but Jarvis Book-binders (Thanet) Ltd of Ramsgate is one of the very few traditional commercial bookbinders left in the county. Catering for both private and wholesale trade it still uses traditional hand techniques. Originally trading under the name of R. J. Burgess, Mr Albert Jarvis took the premises in the 1930s. John Jarvis joined the firm after leaving school and finally took over the business from his father. From the same workshop, or 'bindery' as a bookbinder's premises are known, the company carries out a complete bookbinding service from a 'one off' to a run of 500 or

Gold leaf is tooled on the spine with hot tools. Here the gold lines at the top and bottom of the title are being applied with a double line roller known as a fillet. All gold leaf work on the curved spine must be applied by hand.

Gold leaf can be impressed on the flat surface of a cloth cover by using a blocking press. This press probably dates from the early years of the century and is of great value where a number of books are being produced.

even 1000 or more and still use many of the tools and equipment that were already old when the business was first established.

In general terms the production of binding falls into the category of 'forwarding', which is the string of operations required to complete the actual binding, and 'finishing', which is the embellishment of the cover with decoration and title. Perhaps it is because of the effort frequently put into the finishing, that bookbinding is often regarded as an art rather than a craft. Many bookbinders do have some artistic ability but most traditional bookbinders refer to themselves as tradesmen rather than artists. Whether the book is hand bound or machine bound, the object is the same, i.e. to hold together the leaves in proper order, to protect those leaves when held together and to identify the contents within the binding by titling.

In days gone by, the craft of bookbinding was subdivided even further, each craftsman specialising in a different stage of the process. For example, folding is a task traditionally carried out by women where each sheet was individually folded by hand with absolute precision. In the middle of the last century, folders achieved a remarkable speed, a good worker folding some 500 octavo sheets

per hour. Today in a small bindery each craftsman must have the ability to carry out the 50 or so separate intricate processes such as cutting, mitreing, pressing, sizing, gilding, sewing, rounding, banding, leather paring, tooling, pasting, inlaying, and so on that are required in the trade.

Apart from binding and casing new books, the bookbinders' services are required for binding such items as Law Reports for solicitors, yearly volumes of professional journals, account books, etc. With a renewed interest in antiquarian books over the last few years much of the bookbinder's time is taken up with repair and restoration work. In 1982 John Jarvis's firm worked on an antiquarian local guide book which was to be presented to the Queen Mother on her visit to the Isle of Thanet.

Bookbinding is a skill that cannot be hurried. The craftsmen cannot afford to make mistakes for they work with expensive materials such as high quality blemish-free leather and gold leaf.

Mr Greenstreet outside his shop at 18 Bench Street, Dover in the late 1920s.

THE BOOT-MAKER

Until the beginning of the last century most towns and villages in Kent had their own independent boot-makers. Most folk would have a new pair of boots made every year for obviously in pre motor car days, items of footwear were of extreme importance. Soon hand production began to decline because even quite early on in the Victorian Era, boots could be made entirely by machine, with Northampton becoming the centre of the industry. However, according to a publication of 1866, Edenbridge on the Kent/Surrey border was famed for its production of hob nailed boots which, as the volume states were 'so much worn by waggoners and others'.

An interesting reminder of boot-making in Maidstone is the famous 6ft golden Wellington boot still mounted as a trade sign outside the Golden Boot shoeshop in Gabriels Hill. The business was founded in 1790 and the original site was at number 36 Gabriels Hill opposite the present shop. In 1845 workshops were opened in Palace Yard where 20 craftsmen were employed making 50% of the stock sold in the shop and it is thought that it was then that the famous Wellington Boot was mounted on the front of the building.

The Golden Boot at Gabriels Hill, Maidstone. This famous trade sign dates from the 1840s and is a reminder of the days when the company had workshops in Palace Yard and were producing a good part of the stock. The business has been in the same family for 7 generations.

Cutting out leather round a template on the cutting block.

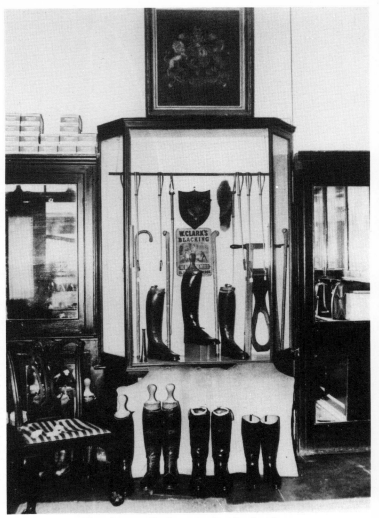

The elegant display case inside the shop.

In the 1980s the majority of boots sold in England are imported from abroad and to find a bespoke boot-maker who will actually make a pair of boots on the premises is something of a rarity.

The business of Messrs J & F Greenstreet of Dover was established in 1820 in the days when most towns supported more than one boot-maker. The original premises were in Snargate Street, once a premier shopping street in the town. In 1899 the Company moved to 18 Bench Street, and a few years ago moved into Victoria Crescent.

Mr Frederick Greenstreet, the 4th generation of Greenstreets, started in the business at the age of 18 and was running the business at the age of 21. Mr Greenstreet has followed his firm's tradition by specialising in Naval, Military and hunting bootwear and has an impressive list of customers ranging from the Life Guards to film stars.

When the customer enters the shop, which has a satisfying aroma of cut leather, Mr Greenstreet himself appears in his apron to attend them. The first task is to measure the customer's foot to enable the hardwood lasts (wooden models of the feet) to be made together with the supporting trees which are made in four interlocking sections. Every dimension and irregularity of the foot must be faithfully noted and the lasts are made two sizes larger than the foot actually measures.

The first thing the boot-maker has to learn is the customer's requirement. Maybe some will request an exceptionally tight fit round the ankle, others may prefer a looser fit in certain places. Furthermore the maker must take into consideration the purpose for which the boots are to be worn and the posture of the customer.

With these measurements and considerations duly recorded the pattern is carefully drafted.

In the days when the firm had a larger staff, the craft of boot-making was divided into various specialised trades. For example, a craftsmen who cut out the carefully selected seasoned leather was known as the 'clicker', the term probably deriving from the sound of the leather being cut. The 'closer' was the craftsman who trimmed and stitched. Today every part of the process is carried out by Mr Greenstreet right through to the 'blacking up' and 'polishing'.

Boot-making is a craft that will probably not survive in the County. The craft cannot be hurried and a satisfactory boot depends entirely upon the high skill of the craftsman who is responsible for every step, from initial measurement to final fitting. The final product then, is perhaps expensive in comparison with a pair of 'off the shelf' boots — maybe £250 in 1982, plus the cost of the trees. Those who can afford the luxury and comfort of a fitted pair of boots, handcrafted in a traditional style which never seems to date, invariably agree that Mr Greenstreet's boots are a joy to own and a pleasure to wear.

Travelling chair menders in Broomfield Road, Bexleyheath.

THE CHAIR CANER

It was not until Charles II returned to England from France, bringing with him new ideas of fashion, that the heavy oak of English furniture gave way to the use of lighter woods, such as beech and walnut. It was also at this period that cane began to be used with the more fashionable woods for chair seats and backs and for other items of furniture.

Cane chairs became extremely successful for they were cheap to make and light to handle and the cane chair maker soon became a craftsman in his own right. Although canework did not oust the silk and velvet seating on expensive and elaborate pieces of furniture the cane chairs were so successful that the upholsterers' company in 1689 brought a petition against them because their own trade was decaying rapidly in favour of the new product. Their petition was unsuccessful.

The early canework was made in the form of a large mesh which gradually became smaller. Canework went in and out of fashion for several centuries but in Victorian and Edwardian times factory made cane chairs were produced in huge quantities.

One of the few Kentish craftsmen still specialising in canework is Bill Birch who has a workshop on the first floor of an XVIIIth Century coach-house at Tenterden. He was taught the craft as a boy by Fred King whose workshop was in Station Road, Tenterden, and after school each afternoon Bill used to carry out all the odd jobs. Mr King's workshop continued in the town until 1950.

In the XVIIth Century cane was brought in from the Malay peninsular, split into quarters and the pith removed before being split into narrow strips. Today cane comes from Singapore, is split in Germany and imported into England ready for use. Very few tools are needed for canework, a knife and a bodkin are essential and pegs are used to hold the canes firmly in place while weaving. Bill Birch remembers the days when even the pegs were cut by hand from twig wood — usually hazel. As well as using traditional ones Bill Birch has designed his own patterns and jobs at the Tenterden workshop range from the repair of cottage chairs to providing cane screenwork for the Palace of Jeddah.

In Victorian times travelling chair menders were a

Bill Birch, a Wealden craftsman in cane and rushwork, reseating a rush chair. He learnt the craft as a boy and now finds his skills in great demand.

Canework is a slow and meticulous task, demanding the utmost concentration. This chair is being caned in a 'six-way pattern', so called because it is worked in six stages. The last three stages are woven in different directions giving the seat considerable strength.

The tools required for rush and canework are few. Here a pin hammer is being used. It is a beautifully balanced tool with a beechwood, pear-shaped handle.

common sight in Kent. As late as 1964 William Ramsey of Chislehurst at nearly 70 years of age, having learnt the craft at the age of 12, was still recaning chairs on the pavements.

The craft of rushwork has also been with us for several centuries, and at one time rush was one of the cheapest materials. However, British grown rushes have not been used in any quantity for a century and a half, and most of the rushes used in the country today come from Holland and Eastern Europe.

Rush seating became popular again in the XVIIIth and XIXth Centuries and the simple design of William Morris' rush-seated 'Sussex Chair' was one of his most successful designs in the second half of the XIXth Century.

An interesting photograph showing cement casks from Burham being loaded on the Medway. One of the best known cement cask manufacturers was a Mr Hinge of Strood.

THE COOPER

For centuries the coopered cask was the container for a wide variety of products from Kentish trades and industries. The cooper's staves were used to secure products as diverse as cement, fish, apples, putty, nails and cider.

Casks were a neat and easily manageable form of packaging and were immensely strong. They were sturdy enough to withstand constant rough-handling and frequent journeys when everything was manhandled between horse, cart and boat. Furthermore the casks were strong enough to stand the not inconsiderable force of fermenting liquids.

The craft of the cooper probably dates back some 4,500 years when coopered vessels were made by the Egyptians and the art was probably introduced into Britain by the Romans, although it declined with their departure. However, it was reintroduced by the Anglo Saxons and attained perfection at a very early period.

Until the mid-XXth Century, coopering was a relatively widespread craft, for nearly every Kentish brewery possessed its own cooper's shop and independent coopers would supply casks to farmers who brewed their own beer and cider. After the late 1950s the only coopers that remained in the county were those employed by the brewers, and their time was spent more on the repair of existing casks than on the actual construction of new casks.

Not only could the cooper make a container from staves of timber and a few iron or wooden hoops that was, without glue, absolutely watertight, but the old time cooper worked without plans, drawings or mathematical calculations. He seemed to work by instinct alone to make the casks that were, as the coopers used to say, 'within an egg-cup' of a predetermined capacity.

In the brewing trade the coopers made casks of various capacities: Butt — 106 (occasionally 108) gallons, Hogshead — 54 gallons, Barrel — 36 gallons, Kilderkin — 18 gallons, Firkin — 9 gallons, Pin — 4½ gallons.

In the middle of the last century the word barrel was a commercial term of measure for various products. Although a beer barrel contained 36 gallons, a barrel of potash would contain 200 lbs, a barrel of gunpowder or a barrel of raisins was 1 cwt, a barrel of herrings 32 gallons and a barrel of Kent cobnuts 3 bushels.

The craft of coopering is hard, strenuous work, a process of constant shaving, scraping and shaping. Oak is the wood used for the staves. In the XVIth Century there was a huge demand for oak and the Weald was supplying oak for ship building and for charcoal which provided fuel for iron furnaces. With the establishment of hop growing on a commercial scale, England was exporting considerable quantities

The cooperage at Messrs Shepherd Neame's Brewery, Faversham in the 1940s. Left — Hollowing out a stave. Right — driving on a metal hoop with a hoop driver and a 4lb hammer.

The cooper at Whitbread's Brewery. On the right is a 'raised up' cask and in the foreground the long jointer plane. (Note the similarity with the XVIth Century illustration.) The cooper is bevelling the head with a curved draw-shave known as a heading knife.

of home-brewed beer and there was some concern over the thousands of oak barrels exported never to be returned, and plans were made towards timber conservation.

However, Wealden grown oak has not been used in the Kentish cooperages in any great quantity for many years. American grown oak, growing south of a latitude of 50°, was preferred and also Russian and German oak was much sought after. There was even some prejudice against the use of English oak as some coopers felt that it gave beer a bad taste. Great care was always taken in the selection of the oak which would be carefully converted into the staves. Such was the quality of oak demanded by the cooper that often other craftsmen would buy used staves from old casks for their own purposes, and as early as 1324 there is a record of barrel staves being sold to Masons for making rules and squares.

The tools of the cooper are of particular interest. They had their own patterns of draw knives and a number of other specialised tools of some antiquity in design, quite unlike those used in any other wood craft. The cooper rarely worked at a bench, for even if he had one, the bench was simply a handy platform for his tools as most of the work was carried out on the floor.

The staves are fitted edge to edge so the joints must be carefully planed to be radial to the centre of the cask, and each is accurately fitted to make a watertight joint with its

8

Knocking down a truss hoop with a trussing adze.

Shaping timber for staves — a process known as listing. The cooper's adze which has a 10" or 11" blade has an off-set haft so the user's knuckles are not knocked against the stave.

XVIth Century Coopers. Note the long jointer plane in the foreground used for shaving the staves.

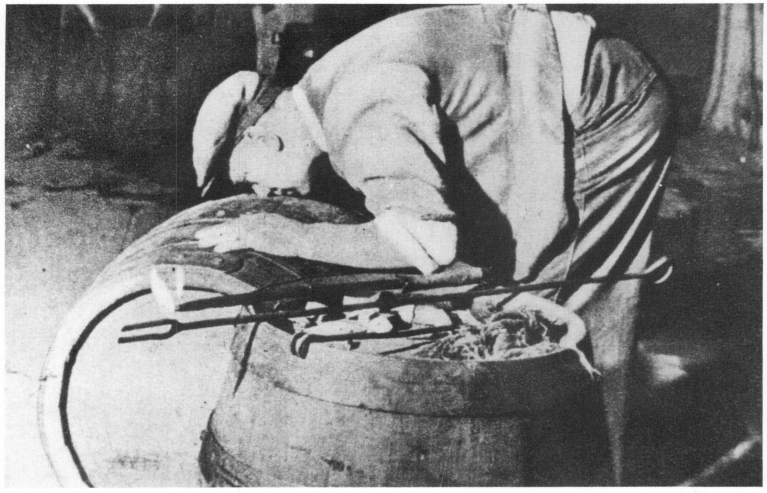

The 'smeller' at Messrs Whitbread's ensures that the cask is sweet by using his nose as well as his eyes.

Washing casks is another task for the cooperage.

In agricultural areas the village coopers of Kent would no doubt have been called upon to make miniature casks variously known as costrels, bever barrels, harvest bottles etc. They had a capacity varying between a quart and a gallon and were used by shepherds, waggoners and other farm workers. The costrel dates from the Middle Ages. The use declined during the First World War when the farm workers found it difficult to cope with the increase in beer duties. The projection on the bung-stave had the dual purpose of housing the leather thong or rope and formed a mouth piece for consuming the contents without having to use a cup.

Whitbread's cooperage. The cooper on the left is chiming the cask using a chiv which levels the inside surface to receive a groove to take the head.

neighbour. Furthermore each stave had to be hollowed and dressed in such a fashion that it was tapered equally above and below the 'bouge' which is the circumference of the greatest diameter.

To bend the stave into the traditional 'bow' shape, the cooper lit a fire of shavings in a small iron brazier known as a cressett (often constructed from old hoop irons) the heat making the staves pliable. Strong ash truss hoops are hammered down over the cask and the ends pinched in with smaller truss hoops. Trussing is usually a two-man job and has to be carried out quickly, for the longer the process takes, the more difficult it is.

The stave ends are levelled and then bevelled with a short handled adze and a circular plane known as a chiv. A 'V' shape groove to receive the head and base is made with another circular plane known as a croze. Obviously the cooper had a wide range of chivs and crozes of varying arcs in shape to match the diameter of the particular cask being constructed.

The heads are made from oak boards dowelled together and for centuries split rushes or 'flags' have been inserted between the boards to prevent leakage.

Finally iron hoops are driven down from each end of the cask, the cooper taking pride in ensuring that the hoops are not only perfectly parallel but also that each hoop is equidistant from either end.

Over the past couple of decades with the high price of timber and the cost of repairing damaged casks, metal casks have replaced wood in Kentish breweries. These are obviously easier to clean, for wood, being slightly porous,

is difficult to sterilise. Indeed washing barrels was often a large part of the cooperage operation. Metal casks are also lighter, but wood, being a poor conductor, insulates beer from the heat rather more efficiently.

The occupation of the cooper is divided into several distinct branches, the wet cooper making casks for liquids, the dry cooper making casks for materials such as flour, tobacco and crockery. The dry coopers' casks were less exacting in structure than other branches of coopering, although no less important, for they were often discarded immediately after use. The bulge was rather less than that of the casks made by the wet cooper and the staves were often of Douglas fir rather than oak.

The tight dry cooper made casks for powdered products such as gunpowder, and the staves were occasionally tongued and grooved for a tight joint. The white cooper made pails, butter churns, wash tubs and other staved utensils for the home and dairy, and often used ash and sycamore as well as oak.

As early as 1875, casks were made by quite sophisticated machines and one London cooperage in that year calculated that the cost of making 600 hogsheads per week by hand labour was 4s 8½d each, whilst the cost of making them by machinery was 1s 10d each. Either boys or unskilled workmen could operate the machines which cut out, shaped and fitted staves, cut, punched and splayed the hoops, planed, ovalled and bevelled the heads and so on, whereby every portion of the cask was fitted with mathematical accuracy and the completed work was as strong and tight as anything that was turned out by the most skilled hand labour.

11

Checking the stock's length on one of a matched pair of twelve bore guns being made at Greenfields workshops in Canterbury.

THE GUNSMITH

Hand guns as opposed to cannon were probably introduced into England about 1471 when Edward IV brought into the country forces which included 300 Flemings armed with hand guns. This would indicate that the craft of gun making was established well before the bow and arrow went out of fashion.

The first guns were fired by applying a light to the touch-hole, but this hazardous method was superceded by the wheel-lock in the XVIth Century and the English flint-lock which appeared in the XVIIth Century. The XIXth Century saw the percussion lock and in 1872 the first true hammerless gun was patented by Theo. Murcott of 68 Haymarket, London.

The gunsmith is a craftsman who, for obvious reasons, must endeavour to be a perfectionist, for there can be no compromise whatsoever, and a well made gun is regarded by a sportsman as both a work of art and a tool that is a pleasure to handle.

One of the very few traditional gun makers practising in this corner of England is the long established firm of Messrs H.S. Greenfield & Son of Canterbury. In 1690 gun barrels were actually being made in the City by Lott in Ivy Lane and guns and pistols still exist made by other Canterbury makers, such as Shepherd in 1770 and Green in 1830. Other names of Kentish gunsmiths appearing on firearms still in existence are Dawes 1780, Jackson 1832 and Oliver 1780, all from Maidstone, Henneker from Chatham 1832

A Lydd stock maker 'sighting up' a rifle stock.

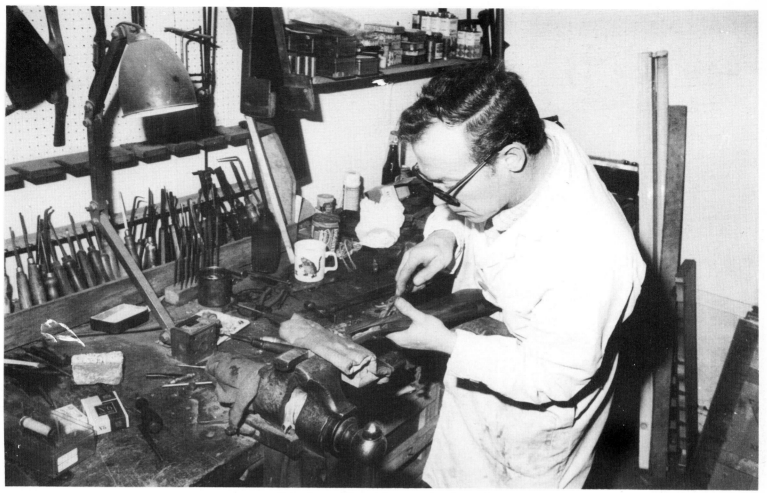

Inletting a rifle stock to receive the action.

Selecting a piece of French walnut from Greenfield's selection of blanks from which a gun stock will be fashioned. Most of the wood is purchased direct from overseas growers.

and Chapman of Cranbrook in 1830. Messrs H.S. Greenfield & Son can trace their firm back many years for they were already making guns in 1805, the year of the Battle of Trafalgar and are still making sporting guns today.

In earlier days gun making was divided into many specialised aspects of the craft, such as lock filers, barrel makers, stock makers, engravers and so on. Today the gunsmith has to be rather more versatile and although many of his machined fittings are obtained from specialist suppliers he still has to have a thorough knowledge of every part of the gun and it often takes many many months to build one piece.

The process of gun making begins with the customer who has to be meticulously measured, for guns are made to fit the client. Perhaps one of the most interesting aspects of gun making is the making of the stock, the size and shape of which have a most significant effect on accuracy.

The most sought-after wood for stock making is carefully selected French walnut, although walnut from Italy, Turkey, Russia, Australia and China is also used. In the past maple has been favoured because of its attractive figuring and ash has also been used for sporting guns. In the mid-XVIth Century beech was used on cheaper guns and also the wild service, usually known as the chequer tree in Kent. Walnut is tough, close-grained, extremely workable and holds its colour and shape well. In addition it is handsome and most gunstockers say that it is imposs- ible to find another wood in the world with so many

An Edenbridge gunsmith

A pair of percussion travelling pistols by W. Green of Canterbury circa 1830. The case also contains the original turnscrew (Victorian word for screwdriver), bullet mould, caps, powder flask, oil bottle and cleaning rod.

qualities as a well seasoned block of even grained walnut. However to find such a piece with all the right qualities is difficult and the price of a perfect piece is high — in 1982 perhaps £500 or more for just a piece of the best wood without any work.

The procedure of gun stocking begins with roughly sawing the butt of walnut to pattern. Accounts from the Canterbury gunsmiths reveal that in 1869 standard rates for sawing out a gun stock was a standard 2d (2 old pence) each, e.g. —

To sawing out 20 gun stocks	3s 4d
To sawing out 94 gun stocks	15s 8d
To sawing out 260 gun stocks	£2 3s 4d

and so on.

The rough sawn out butt is held in the vice and the stocker pares away with a broad short bladed chisel. Old time gun stockers often used an old gun stock instead of a mallett for tapping the chisel. The stock gradually takes shape through a process of draw shaves, spoke shaves and rasps. The stock must be exact in all three dimensions, for it is essential that the downward curve and the length and the angle to the shoulder are made to fit perfectly. Generally the taller the customer, the longer and more crooked the stock should be. There should also be an inclination outwards to allow for the swell of the chest, as the eye cannot, without considerable difficulty, be placed correctly

in line with the centre of the shoulder. The broader the chest, the more the stock should be inclined outwards.

Recesses for the action and furniture are marked and neatly chisled out. One method often used by the old gunsmiths when cutting out the rebate was to hold the metal part to be inserted in the flame of a candle or a paraffin lamp to 'smoke' it and then place the part in the stock. The heavy soot deposit left a pronounced mark on the wood thus indicating exactly where the wood needed further easing.

The final product whether shotgun or rifle is balanced and matched perfectly to the customer's body so that aiming, as the gun makers say, is as natural a movement as pointing a finger.

Packing canisters at Messrs John Hall & Sons, Gunpower Works, Faversham, in about 1925.

THE KENTISH GUNPOWDER INDUSTRY

Faversham was one of the first towns in England to produce gunpowder on any scale. The town was certainly producing the product in the reign of Elizabeth I and maybe even earlier. At the time of the Napoleonic Wars, the industry was of such importance that one in four of Faversham's male population was employed at the gunpowder mills.

Gunpowder was composed of a mixture of sulphur, salt petre and charcoal and the manufacture involved a process of mixing, crushing, sieving and drying. It was dependent upon such craftsmen as the charcoal burner and the mill-wright for the safe upkeep of the mill.

Faversham was an ideal centre for the industry. Wood was available for the huge quantity of charcoal required and being a port it could easily receive the other two essential ingredients, sulphur and salt petre, which came from abroad. Water was also required in huge quantities for power and was also used for the transportation of the product.

The value of the gunpowder depended considerably upon the quality of the charcoal and so the industry insisted on charcoal totally free from extraneous particles. Ideally, the charcoal was used as quickly as possible after preparation.

Until 1760 the Army and Navy were purchasing gunpowder from private firms but in that year the government bought what was known as the Home Works which became the first Royal Gun Powder factory. The mills were duly extended and fifteen years later with eleven water mills and five horse work mills in operation, this particular works was producing 364 tons of gunpowder per annum.

Powder punts carrying gunpowder in the Marsh Works, Faversham. For obvious reasons it was safer to carry by water when the only other method of transport involved horses where there was the danger of sparks being struck from their iron shoes.

Where it was not possible to carry gunpowder by water, the powder wagons had to be covered and the load carefully protected.

Chart Mills. Restored by the Faversham Society in 1969.

Canister making, Oare Gunpowder Works, in about 1925.

Explosions

Workers in the gunpowder mills were under the constant threat of explosion although there did not appear to be any difficulty in obtaining workmen. Many precautions were taken, e.g. the mill house roofs were covered with soft wood boarding with weak fastenings so that when an explosion occurred the blast met with little resistance in the hope that the damage would be limited to blowing off the roof. Other precautions were that workers wore slipper-like shoes, hand sewn with no nails, gunpowder kegs were wiped over with a soft brush before they were moved to remove any grit that might be adhering, and trees were planted in carefully selected positions in the hope of reducing the effect of any blast. All hinges were well oiled, cogs and axles soaped and oiled and to avoid dangerous friction, provision was made to stop ropes rubbing against wood. Even the wheelbarrow wheels were rimmed with copper instead of iron and later other precautions were installed, such as water tanks, which, in the event of explosion, would empty and flood the mills automatically.

Sadly explosions did occur. In 1767 an explosion at the Home Works caused damage to Davington Priory. Fourteen years later at the same works an explosion was heard in London. Explosions were not confined to the Faversham Works for at Richard Archer's old paper-making mill at Dartford, which was converted into a gunpowder mill in the XVIIIth Century, there were also many explosions; eleven lives being lost in 1795 and eight in 1833.

Faversham — the world's first gun cotton town

After the Napoleonic Wars, there was a decline in the demand for gunpowder and in 1825 the Home Works was sold for nearly £18,000 to John Hall of Dartford who founded the well known Dartford firm of J.E. Hall Limited. In 1846 John Hall & Sons, who were then operating from the Marsh Works, obtained patent rights for producing gun-cotton, thus making Faversham the first gun-cotton manufacturing town in the world. The expense of gun-cotton is rather greater than that of gunpowder because of the difficulty and danger in its manufacture for it is liable to spontaneous ignition or decomposition by keeping. Sadly, there was another explosion in 1847 with the loss of twenty lives.

In 1874, a formula was evolved whereby the purest gun-cotton was crushed to a dust and incorporated with an equal weight of the nitrate of baryta. The powder was moulded by powerful machinery at a pressure of over five tons per square inch into solid cartridges of a diameter suitable for blasting. The material was patented by George Trench from Faversham and was marketed under the name of 'Tonite'. The material has been used for many years for signalling as the cartridges, when set free, burn with a brilliant greenish flame. Although the manager of the Faversham factory wrote in 1875:

"The word Tonite is a misnomer altogether and ought never to be used, the proper title for the explosive being

The Oare Works, Faversham, left to right. Bert Swan, a process man, R. Wise, a charge hand and P. Croucher, the boatman/service waiter who were later killed in an explosion at the works in 1916.

'cotton powder' and which is also the orginal term, and has never been discontinued."
the name was used for many decades.

Towards the end of the XIXth Century the area covered by gunpowder producers in the Faversham district extended to about 250 acres. Charcoal at this time was being made by the firms themselves and was being burnt in large iron cylinders where the charcoal was found to be less contaminated than that produced in the forest in the traditional clamps.

The industry continued in the XXth Century. One explosives factory at Uplees contained over 200 buildings and at the beginning of the First World War high explosive ammunition was filled in the area. On April 2nd 1916 disaster struck again in the form of a huge TNT explosion in which over 100 employees were tragically killed.

In the inter-war years the industry rapidly declined but the town still bears traces of the industry, including the Chart Mills which were restored in 1969 by the active Faversham Society.

THE KENTISH PAPER-MAKERS

Turkey Mill in the 1980s.

Until about 1960, rags were still the basic materials used for paper-making and were supplied from textile mills and also from rag merchants. The photograph shows rag collecting in Gravesend. Today, with the shortage of cotton rags because of the increased use of synthetic materials, cotton linters, manila and flax pulps are used.

The craft of paper-making was introduced into Kent in Elizabethan times and to this day, Kent is still a notable paper-making county, having more paper mills than any other county in the British Isles.

One of the early successful paper mills was established at Dartford on the River Darent in about 1588, by John Spilman who was jeweller to Queen Elizabeth I. He was granted a patent for the manufacture of white writing paper, which forbade any other person making paper for ten years, and a licence giving him the monopoly of collecting rags, leather shreds, parchment scraps, old fishing nets, and other paper making materials within the Kingdom. The Mill was successful and it was reputed that, at one time, some 600 men were employed there. King James I inspected the Mill in 1605 and duly conferred a knighthood on Spilman.

Soon the industry was successfully established, for the Kentish rivers provided power to pound rags into pulp, and springs, which were often found nearby, provided the huge supplies of pure water necessary for paper-making. Many paper mill sites date back to far earlier times when they were originally used as fulling mills or corn mills. The river-bank position also helped with transport.

At the beginning of the XVIIth Century there were some 120 vats within sixty miles of London, supplying some 75% of the 400,000 reams of paper then used annually by the country. Mills were widely established throughout Kent including sites at Eynsford, Buckland near Dover, Shoreham, possibly at Goudhurst and many around Maidstone. Later in the century brown paper, which was made from sails, old ropes, wagon covers etc. was being made at Canterbury and to this day a paper mill remains at Chartham on the Stour near Canterbury. In 1798, the water here was said to be 'far superior to any in the County'.

The famous Turkey Mill at Maidstone still stands on the River Len, a tributary of the Medway to the East of the Town. For nearly three centuries the Turkey Mill produced paper and during its middle period, had a world-wide reputation. Like many other mills it started life as a fulling mill in 1640, and changed to a paper mill in 1693 under the ownership of George Gill, a member of the old Boxley family. William Gill was bankrupted in 1729, probably because of competition from imported paper from the London market, but Richard Harris acquired the mill together with Turkey Court in 1736. His widow Anne married James Whatman in 1740, thus introducing into Turkey Mill one of the most celebrated names in the paper-making industry throughout the world.

James Whatman, a former officer of the Kent Militia, had learnt the craft in Holland and his efforts of paper-making in Maidstone were a success. After his death in 1759 the more famous James Whatman Junior took over the business at the age of 18 and extended the mill. By improving the technique of white paper manufacture, he enhanced the mill's reputation even further and by 1774 the mill was described as 'the most complete in the Kingdom'. The mill continued to produce paper throughout the XIXth Century under the Hollingworth family and their successors and did not close until the 1970s.

During the XVIIIth Century paper-makers operating from some of the small mills were often also dependent upon other occupations. For example, in 1766 one paper-maker, Simon Pine of Otham, was also a miller which was probably

SPRINGFIELD MILL, MAIDSTONE circa 1910

RAG SORTING. Rags were carefully graded and zips, elastic, buttons, etc had to be removed. As early as the 17th century the demand for rags outweighed the supply and during the 19th century the rag shortage was so critical that the Royal Society of Arts sponsored the use of alternative materials.

THE CHESTS. The wet pulp passed to the chest where it was stirred continuously which prevented the fibre settling. The pulp was then directed from the chest to the vats.

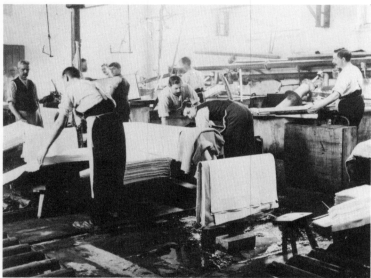

THE VAT HOUSE. The paper-maker on the right handling the mould was known as the vatman. The coucher, second from right, carefully inverted the mould face downwards onto the paper-maker's felt.

THE SIZING DEPARTMENT. The size bath machine in operation. The sheets passed through a weak solution of high grade gelatine after which they were sent to the drying loft.

THE DRYING LOFT. The paper was dried by hanging the sheets on cowhair rope which avoided marking the sheets. Paper in its unsized state is known as 'waterleaf'.

THE FINISHING ROOM. It often took from three to twelve months for a sheet of paper to be processed through the mill to the finishing room where the paper was sorted, counted and packed.

The vatmen at Hayle Mill. Over half a century separate these two photographs, the illustration on the left shows Arthur Watmore and that on the right Cyril Thomas.

not unusual, for both crafts were dependent upon water power. However, what is, perhaps, more surprising is that Mr Pine was also a hop planter. Similarly, in 1878, Thomas Budgen a paper-maker of Dartford, was also a currier.

Another famous paper-making name in the area is that of the Balston family of Springfield Mill. The original William Balston worked with James Whatman at Turkey Mill from 1774 and stayed on at the Mill after Whatman's share had been sold to the Hollingworth brothers.

In 1805, William Balston purchased a riverbank site along the Medway and built a ten vat mill. He named his paper mill 'Springfield Mill' for the attraction of the site was not the river for water power but the availability of pure spring water. His mill, at that time, not only had more vats than any other mill in the county, but Balston also installed one of James Watt's earliest steam engines which was supervised by James Watt himself, and became the first paper mill to be driven by steam. In 1834 steam power was being installed at a paper mill near Dover and soon William Joynson's famous mill at St Mary Cray had eight steam engines. Basted Mill near Borough Green had a steam powered paper-making machine in 1836, but the beaters were driven by water power and at that time, the mill's water wheel was the largest in the country.

Balston's Springfield Mill was destroyed by fire in 1862 but was immediately rebuilt and remained purely a vat mill for one and a quarter centuries, for it was not until 1931 that a paper-making machine was installed.

Messrs W and R Balston had the sole rights to make paper under the trade name of James Whatman and the paper produced at Springfield Mill became famous throughout the world. The mill passed through the Balston family for many generations and there was a Balston in the business until 1981 when Hugh Balston retired. In the 1980s the mill is still producing specialised paper, trading under the name of Whatman.

The XIXth Century saw the introduction of the paper-making machine which was developed with the enthusiastic help of Bryan Donkin, who was at one time apprenticed with Hall, the Dartford engineer. Census returns for 1851 reveal that there were more people involved in the paper-making industry in Kent than in any other county, with 981 men and 1,423 women involved in the industry.

With the removal of tax on paper, further encouragement was given to the large mills. For example, in Dartford in 1862 the Ettrick Forest Mill was built, becoming in 1866 'The Daily Telegraph Paper Mill' and in the early part of the century, had a housing estate built for workers. Paper-making continues on a large scale in North Kent where there are still abundant supplies of clean water. Various mills of the county produced hundreds of miles of newsprint, greaseproof paper, household tissue, cement bags, corrugated paper, tracing paper etc. etc.

Over the years, the Kentish mills producing hand made paper have gradually closed down. Some changed their products to meet different demands — an example being Eynsford Mill which dates from 1648 and had a reputation for high grade hand made paper until recent times. During the war, many of the staff were recalled from retirement, and during those troubled years, helped with the manufacture of gas detector sleeves, insulating material for aircraft wires and even cigarette papers for the French forces.

In the 1980s there is just one mill left in the county making hand made paper by traditional methods. At Hayle Mill in the Loose Valley, near Maidstone, high quality paper continues to be made for the Barcham Green family by craftsmen, with hardly any change in the basic method of production since the industry was introduced to Kent some 4 centuries ago.

The first of a long line of paper-makers with the name of Green, was John Green who was born near Gravesend in 1699. In 1810 the fourth generation of paper-making Greens moved from East Malling to Hayle Mill, where the descendants of the original John Green are still continuing the family tradition.

Paper is made into sheets by means of a mould and deckle. The mould consists of a hardwood frame covered at the top with a wire cloth. The deckle which is used in conjunction with the mould, is a frame with the outer dimension corresponding to the size of the mould and the inside corresponding to the size of the sheet of paper; the purpose being to contain the pulp on the wire cloth. When the deckle is placed on the wire of the mould, it forms a shallow sieve in which the paper-maker takes up a quantity of the pulp. With a skilful shake of the mould and deckle the sheet is consolidated and the water drains through leaving the pulp in the form of a sheet on the wire. The deckle is removed and the mould is passed to the Coucher who carefully inverts the mould onto the paper-maker's felt. The newly couched sheet is covered with another felt and the mould is returned to the vatman who, by now, has another sheet using a second mould, and the original deckle. This procedure continues until a 'post' of sheets, usually about 80 - 100, has been made. Paper-making can involve lifting an amazing 25 tons of water from a vat during a single day.

Den Burford — the beaterman at Ford Mill. He prepares the raw materials in such a way that the sheet of flong that is formed will have the highest quality. The paddle he is using is known as the beaterman's 'stool' or 'crutch'.

THE VILLAGE MILL THAT KEEPS FLEET STREET ROLLING

Another particularly interesting village paper mill is Ford Mill situated in the centre of Little Chart, a tiny Kentish village with not much more than a hundred rated properties. This unique mill produces a special paper product known as 'flong' which is essential to the newspaper industry where letterpress printing is often still used.

It is thought that the mill was originally a wool mill, but was making paper for many centuries until the 1940s when it was still producing hand made papers, especially security papers for cheques, documents, etc.

Flong is a kind of cardboard produced as a number of layers of paper sandwiched together to make a composite sheet. When a newspaper page is 'passed for press' the forme of type is taken to the stereotyping department where the flong is placed over it and subjected to considerable pressure in a moulding press, thus forming an impression on the flong. The resulting mould is dried and, because flong is flexible, it can be bent into a semi-circular shape and used as a pattern into which molten metal can be poured, thus forming a curved replica of the original flat forme. These plates are clamped on a rotary printing press which can be run at very high speeds — maybe 60 - 70,000 impressions per hour.

Flong obviously has to be highly compressible when wet and rigid when dry. It is made in a discontinuous manner because of the enormous strength needed to withstand the pressure needed to form the moulded relief and also to withstand the heat of molten metal.

The process of stereo-typing by taking a mould and then casting a number of plates has been used in Holland since about 1700 when gypsum was probably used for casting. The process of using flexible flong paper was introduced to England in the mid XIXth Century. During the earlier part of this century the material was imported, much of it from Germany. There was a shortage of the material during the war so Lord Beaverbrook instigated the manufacture of flong in Great Britain and an agreement was made with this Kentish Mill. Since those days the process has become rather more sophisticated, and the exercise has progressed but is still dependent upon local craftsmen. The Mill is the only one in the U.K. and exports the material as far as Australia. It is material from this Kentish village mill that literally keeps the newspaper presses rolling.

Edwin Amies' old premises on the corner of Mote Road and Chancery Lane.

Making laid wire on a loom that was made by Messrs Edwin Amies in 1889 and is still used today.

PAPER MILL ENGINEERS

Mould making

A craft closely connected with paper-making is the construction of the mould and deckle and the old established firm of Messrs Edwin Amies & Co are now the only commercial hand mould makers in the western world. The mould is usually made of mahogany with boxwood reinforcements and with ribs of yellow pine. Each section is shaped individually and dove-tail corner joints made. For what are known as 'laid' papers, the top of the mould frame consists of a number of parallel wires stretched across the frame close together with other finer wires strung in pairs at right angles and twisted around the laid wires often about an inch apart. Laid paper can be recognised by the ribbed appearance and the laid wire is still made on a special mahogany and brass loom built by Messrs Edwin Amies & Co in 1889.

In what is known as a 'wove' paper a woven wire cloth is stretched over the mould frame. Fixing the wire onto the mould involves intricate sewing, patience, a steady hand and keen eyesight.

The deckle for the last hundred years or so, has been made from mahogany although other woods had been used previously. The cross-section of the wood is formed with special moulding planes and the pieces profiled to give the

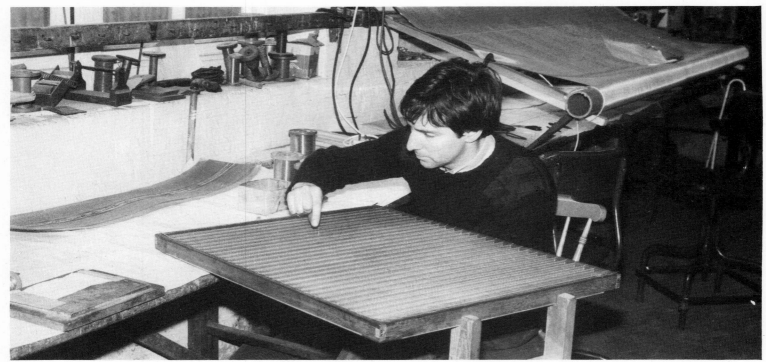

Martyn Rolfe working on a hand mould.

best performance. The frame corners are bound with brass. Such is the craftsmanship of the mould and deckle that they rarely wear out and some have been in constant daily use for half a century or longer.

Watermarking

The watermark in paper is produced by bending tinned copper wires into the letters or device required which is sewn on to the mould surface. The study of watermark symbols is a fascinating subject, for the themes may be decorative, religious or purely commercial. Favourite watermarks on papers used by Caxton and other early printers were an ox head, a star, a collared dog's head, a jug, etc. A fool's cap and bells gave its name to foolscap paper and the XVIIIth Century watermark of the post horn — often within a shield — probably gave its name to 'post paper'.

Sewing in the watermark on a cylinder mould cover for machine paper-making.

Both the mould and deckle are re-inforced with brass.

Ron MacDonald sewing in a watermark on a mould for paper used to celebrate the 1977 Queen's Silver Jubilee.

24

The firm of Messrs W.J. Thompson have been established in Ashford throughout 9 reigns. At the turn of the century their business was situated in the High Street and the craft of printing was coupled with that of gold and silver smiths, jeweller and watch & clock maker.

THE KENTISH PRINTER

Although known in China for many centuries, printing was not invented in Europe until the XVth Century. Before this time books were hand written, mostly in Latin, some of the scribes and monks producing beautifully illuminated manuscripts, sometimes taking many years to complete one volume. The cost of these hand written books was extremely high and in the XIVth Century some books would cost as much as £35 — an enormous sum of money at this period. It is not surprising then that books in the universities and churches were chained to walls.

William Caxton was the first English printer and Tenterden in Kent has traditionally been accepted as this brilliant man's birth place, but both Westerham and Hadlow have also made the claim; Hadlow even boasting a thoroughfare named Caxton Lane. Certainly Caxton was of Kent stock, coming from a family of Kentish mercers. He writes in his preface to the 'Historyes sisters of Troy' 'I was born and lerned myn Englissh in Kente in the Weeld where I doubt not is spoken as brode and rude Englissh as in ony place of England.' The Weald at that time was still rather remote for even a century and a half after Caxton was born, the topographer, Lambarde, informs us that it was a 'waste and wilderness not peopled with men but stored and stuffed with herds of deer and droves of hogs'.

It is thought that Caxton was born in 1422 and in 1438 it was recorded that he was apprenticed to Alderman Robert Large, one of London's most eminent mercers. Eventually, Caxton was admitted to the livery of the Mercer's Company and business took him to the Low Countries and for 30 years or so, he lived in or visited Flanders, Holland and the Zeeland. Caxton was certainly successful for he became, in 1454, Governor of the English Merchants at Bruges and a member of the Merchants Adventurers. He frequently returned to England docking at Sandwich which was then a busy port used for the cloth trade and it was thought that he had relations in the area.

As governor, Caxton was chosen by Edward IVth to negotiate renewal of trade between Burgundy and England. The first mission was unsuccessful, the Duke of Burgundy prohibiting the sale of English cloth in his domain and it became Caxton's task to enforce the new English law forbidding the importation of flemish goods. The Duke died in 1467 and the following year his son, Charles, married Margaret the sister of Edward IVth and a new and successful trade treaty was agreed.

Later, Caxton resigned from his post as governor and took up a new position as advisor to Margaret, now the Duchess of Burgundy. During his period as governor Caxton

The printer stands in front of his cases of type which stand on a tilted bench, and drops each letter individually into the composing stick. Left: Theo Clarke. Right: W. James Thompson
Note the poster remaining on the side of Mr Thompson's bench which was printed by his grandfather in 1879.

had tried to find time to translate the 'Historyes of Troy' and as Margaret also had a great interest in the arts, she encouraged him to persevere with his translation. The work was finally completed and the manuscript presented to the Duchess on 19th September 1471.

During translation, Caxton had promised copies to several friends and by the time he had laboriously finished his third book, he felt he could write no more without ruining his eyesight. He records that his eyes were 'dimed with over much loking on the whit paper'.

In the 1460s a printing press had been set up in Cologne by the priest Ulrich Zell and it was at this press that Caxton had learnt the craft of printing and had met Wynkyn de Worde who was later to become Caxton's chief assistant and successor. In 1472, the year after Caxton had completed the translation of the Historyes of Troy he returned to Bruges and set up his own press.

Caxton was an astute businessman and his carefully chosen subject matter sold well. The first book to be printed in the English language (Caxton's 'Brode and Rude Kentish English) was, of course, his favourite 'The Historyes of Troy', in 1474, followed in 1475 by 'The Game and Play of Chess'.

In the autumn of 1476 Caxton returned to England and set up the first English Press near Westminster Abbey where now stands Tothill Street, and the first item to be printed in England was a letter of Indulgence issued by the Abbott of Abingdon to Henry and Kathleen Langley of London. In November 1477 the first book to be printed in England was presented to Edward IV. This was the first of many titles and when Caxton died in 1491 this remarkable man had printed some 100 books. On the day of his death he had just completed the last page of the translation of 'Life of Our Fathers'.

Titles printed by Caxton include Canterbury Tales, Morte d'Arthur, Aesop's Fables, and his largest book the 'Golden Legend' containing 894 pages. An original copy of the 'Polychonicon' which Caxton translated from the Latin in 1481 (all 340,000 words) was presented to the Town of Tenterden in 1928 by an American collector.

Caxton's assistant Wynkyn de Worde continued the printing business eventually moving to Fleet Street and by the time he died in 1535 he had printed 800 items and had earned the title of 'Father of Fleet Street'.

In 1549 John Mychell printed the first book at Canterbury, a theological work followed by several other works of a theological nature. There seems to be no record of any other printers in the City, apart from a XVIth Century monastic printer at St Augustine's, until the Kentish Post was produced on the 23rd October, 1717. Maidstone had a press in 1701 and in 1707 published a theological work by J Bernard the Vicar of Ospringe, near Faversham.

The early printers had to have a knowledge of many specialised techniques for they had to be type founders, publishers, editors, engravers, book sellers and ink makers. Printers' ink consisted of lamp black and linseed oil mixed to a treacle like consistency.

The presses were modelled on the old wooden presses and, with a few adaptions, the hand press was used for 350 years. It was a simple wooden screw-press with a handle attached which was lowered to a plate (platen) to press against the inked type to secure an impression and, although the press was improved over the years, it was not until the last century that iron presses were introduced. The first iron press with its improved leverage was by Earl Stanhope followed by the mechanically simple yet extremely powerful Columbian press introduced in 1816, and the Albion press in 1823. There were many of these attractive cast iron presses in use in Kent in the XIXth Century. They were the basic equipment for the jobbing printers producing hand-bills, notices, auctioneers' catalogues, letterheads, etc. and the Columbian press was large enough to take a newspaper forme which could be printed at one pull. A splendid Columbian press was still in regular use at a Kentish village printing works in mid Kent in 1975, functioning perfectly well, and there are other presses of a similar vintage still used occasionally for pulling proofs, producing short runs or for the production of deluxe editions.

The setting up of type probably sounds a simple task but in fact great skill, thorough training and dexterity is required. The type faces are arranged in boxes or 'laid in cases' as the printers say. The upper case is divided into equal spaces, the left-hand division containing capital letters fractions, figures, etc. and the right-hand division small capitals, accented letters, asterisks, etc. The letters and figures are arranged in their alphabetical and numerical order from left to right. The lower case contains the small letters, spaces, stops, commas, etc. but the divisions are unequal, the letters most in request having the largest division, thus letter 'e' has the largest and the letters, j q x and z have the smallest compartment. The whole fount (set of type) amounts to over 150,000 letters, figures, spaces, etc.

The compositor stands before the case which is laid on a tilted bench. He usually places his copy of the manuscript on the part of the upper case which is little used. In his left hand he takes a composing stick which is a small metal frame with an inner moveable sliding portion adjustable by a turn-screw to the exact length of the page-line. The first letter of the first word of the copy is placed followed by the second and so on along the length of the stick with a space in between each word. If the compositor arrives at the end of a line and finds that he cannot complete the word or even a syllable he must still contrive to make the words and spaces fill a line exactly. He can either remove some of the spaces first inserted and replace them with thicker space, or if the last word is only a letter or so short, he can remove some of the thicker spaces and insert thinner ones. The spaces must be managed so that the final printed paper appears balanced, not too light and not too dark.

Gus Clarke using a Columbian press which was introduced in 1816. When photographed in 1975 the press was in every day use in a Mid-Kent printing works. The grand cast iron eagle acted as an adjustable counter-weight.

Correct spacing is the test of a good compositor and the experienced man will, as the work is proceeding, skilfully measure by eye the exact number of words, syllables and spaces the line requires and adjust them accordingly. The process of setting the type to the exact measure is known as justification.

The compositors work rapidly making no unnecessary movements for the work is rather laborious. They remain in a standing position for freedom of action, sometimes composing some 2,000 letters per hour. The compositor will always pick up the correct letter, taking it up by the face-end and before it is actually inserted into the composing stick his eye is directed to the next letter. Whilst his eye is also looking at the copy the mind is working a line or two in advance.

When the composing stick is full, the composed matter is lifted out and placed in a frame known as a galley. This apparently simple operation also requires some skill, for if not properly grasped the stick, full of type, will collapse and form what is known as 'pie'.

On completion of a sheet, the galley is placed on an imposing stone, often a slab of marble, and fastened in a frame (the chase). This is dressed and locked and the completed page is ready for inking.

The compositor was traditionally paid a rate for every estimated 1000 letters composed. In the 1850s a compositor

Each individual piece of type is picked up by hand and placed in the composing stick. An experienced craftsman sometimes composes some 2,000 letters per hour.

would be paid 6d per thousand using standard sized type, ½d more per thousand when working in a foreign language but 8½d per thousand for Greek and a farthing per thousand more for Hebrew and Arabic. This rate included not only the composing and justifying but the making up of the pages, correcting and distributing the type back to the correct cases and boxes after printing. Watching a printer 'dissing' type is fascinating. Holding a quantity of composed type in his left hand, face towards him, he takes out a few words between forefinger and thumb of the right hand and at lightning speed drops each letter into its correct box, a good compositor distributing an incredible 50,000 letters a day.

Mechanical or hot metal typesetting was invented towards the end of the last century and rapidly replaced the hand compositor in most larger printers and newspapers. Over the last twenty years litho, using a photographically produced printing plate, has replaced letterpress as the principal method of printing, except in Fleet Street. This in turn has led to the development of filmsetting, one of the early applications of microchip technology.

The county of Kent is still the centre of the printing industry with several large works concentrated around Tonbridge and the Medway Towns. The old hand craft or letter-press printing is still used in many of the smaller Kentish print shops giving the firm clear print impression, although the number of old style jobbing printers in the county is now dwindling.

Before Caxton set up his press in England books were hand written and could only be produced at enormous cost and it was not surprising that books in the churches and universities were chained. The tradition continued after the introduction of printing. Some of Caxton's work is held at the chained library in Hereford Cathedral.

A Folkestone sign and ticket writer. Examples of his signwriting can be seen on the vehicle and handwritten posters could be produced almost instantly.

The sign makers and signwriters used also to produce show cards, tickets and posters as can be seen by this rare Herne Bay shop front which was installed in the late 1920s by Messrs H.T. Joy & Son.

THE SIGNWRITER

Not so many years ago examples of the signwriters craft were all around us. In any town, before the standardisation of chain-store shop fronts and the availability of plastic lettering, almost every fascia was written by hand.

In earlier days the signwriter was often the sign maker and as well as having the skill to decorate with the brush and paint, also had to have some knowledge of carpentry. Much shop front work was carried out by builders who would employ a man in the carpenter's shop to carve the lettering on fascias which was gilded by the signwriter and covered with plate glass.

Excavations over the last few decades reveal that trade signs were displayed outside the premises of Roman tradesmen, and thus sign making is a craft of some antiquity. In earlier days the sign was simply a pictorial symbol identifying a tradesman's craft, and in the days of illiteracy a pictorial sign was obviously rather more readily understood than a written sign. Pictorial signs were even more common in the days before street numbering was introduced less than two centuries ago. A good example of a XIXth Century trade sign is the famous Golden Boot which can still be seen in Mill Street, Maidstone, illustrated on page three. Certainly these old trade signs must have given the street scene considerable interest and variety.

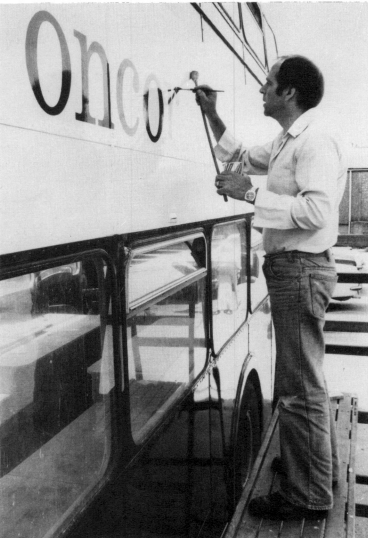

Vehicle painting has been an important aspect of the signwriter's craft from the earliest days of commercial vehicles to the present day.

Ernest Davey mixing his colours with a palette knife. Note the encrustations of paint over the preparation bench that have built up through many decades of signwriters wiping their brushes.

Early examples of the Kentish signwriters craft can be seen in a number of churches, for it was often only the local signwriter who was capable of preparing the coats of arms, funeral 'Hatchments', the beautiful examples of lettering on display panels of the Ten Commandments, the gilding of the church clock faces and hands, and so on.

Another branch of signwriting is poster and ticket writing, and until the 1960s signwriters often used to list themselves as 'sign, poster and ticket writers'. Handwritten posters were, until the 1970s, frequently used outside theatres and picture houses and the shops displayed thousands of hand written tickets depicting sales, special offers, big reductions, price tickets, etc., all neatly hand written usually using red on a white background. Some department stores still maintain display studios today where hand written tickets are produced.

Apart from having natural artistic ability the other essential qualities for the signwriter are fully to understand the principles of layout and design, have some sense of perspective and above all patience.

One well known firm of signwriters along the North Kent coast is Messrs 'Smeeds Smart Signs'. The firm was founded by William Ormond Victor Smeed (the Ormond came from a Derby winner) who started working life as a tiler's apprentice but changed to signcraft in about 1920 in a shed in Culvert Passage at the back of the Herne Bay

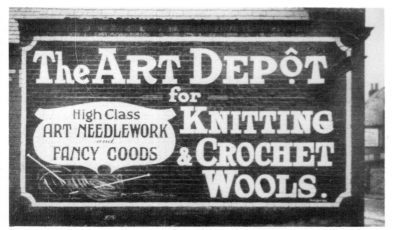

This handpainted panel was painted directly on the wall of a building on the corner of East Street and Mortimer Street, Herne Bay. It was some 20 ft in length and 11 ft high.

31

clock tower. Mr Ernest Davey joined Mr Smeed as an apprentice in 1926 and, with his partner Mr Stan King, is still signwriting in 1982. As with many other signwriters of the 1980s, much of their work is vehicle painting. During the Second World War Mr Davey carried on the craft of signwriting for the army, producing direction signs and so on. He recalls that, with the shortage of material, signs often had to be written on discarded corrrugated iron, which had first to be beaten flat with a hammer. In different countries signs had to be produced in different languages. Mr Davey produced French signs in Algeria, Greek signs in Greece, and in Italy had to paint some signs which he described as 'like shorthand with a lot of tails to it — I didn't know what language it was!' Another signwriter Mr Walter Briscall who ran a well known signwriting business in Ashford for many years was requisitioned in the war to advise on the camouflage of the pillboxes.

Today the number of top quality signwriters is dwindling. Advances have been made in transfer lettering for display purposes which is quicker to execute but, lacks the individuality of the brush stroke.

Another aspect of the signwriter's craft which has not quite gone out of fashion is that of gilding on glass, where the gold leaf is applied to the back of glass (working in reverse) with a water size and afterwards protected by paint.

Painters and signwriters at the premises of William Henry Boyer, the Sandwich photographer. It is interesting to note that the designs of the ladder, the mahl stick and paint kettle are still in regular use 100 years later.

In a signwriter's workshop preparing decorations for the 1953 Coronation Mr W.R. Briscall standing and Mr R. Coney with palette.

SILK PRINTING BY HAND. The printing table, 25 to 30 yards long, is washed down and prepared by spreading glue with a stick. The dried gum prevents the silk from slipping.

Silk printing block.

THE SILK PRINTERS

The Crayford area of what was North West Kent, now a London Borough, has played an important part in the fabric finishing industry for some centuries. The skills of the bleachers and whitesters are initially needed, as textiles that are to be printed or dyed must first be whitened. The whiter the material, the more brilliant and effective the dyes will be.

An abundant supply of pure water is required for bleaching and by the XVIIth Century the bleaching fields south of the Thames were already polluted and some 120 acres of land around Crayford had been prepared where 'there is neither Smoke nor Smut to offend' as one XVIIth Century writer put it.

One of the earliest methods of bleaching was to spread out the material to be whitened on the bleaching grounds and to sprinkle it with pure water several times a day. After several months' exposure to air, light and moisture, the materials were duly bleached. Over the years methods improved and chemical bleaching agents were used. The Crayford bleaching grounds were still in use in the latter half of the XIXth Century.

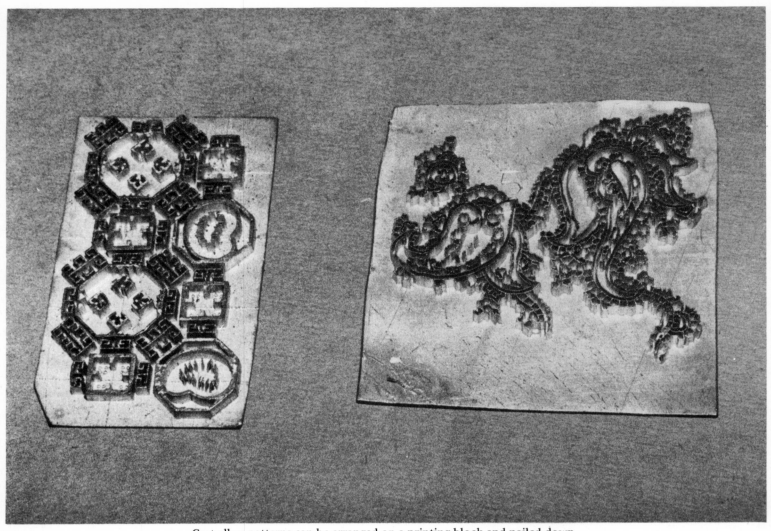

Cast alloy patterns can be arranged on a printing block and nailed down.

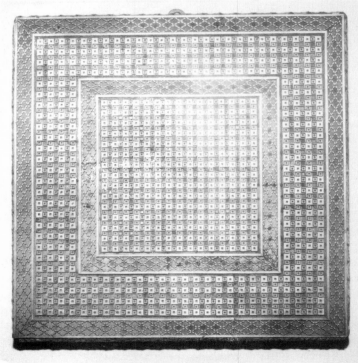

Silk printing block.

It is thought that the actual printing of fabrics was established by the early XVIIIth Century and although at one time there were a number of printing centres in Essex, Surrey and London the industry dwindled after textile printing was introduced in Lancashire in the 1760s. The industry has continued in Crayford without a break into the 1980s.

One of the most famous names in the area known for high quality work was Charles Swaisland who came to Crayford in 1812. He exhibited his products at the Great Exhibition in 1851 and was awarded a prize medal for his 'Printed shawls of great excellence'. One of his designs exhibited required no less than 550 separate printing blocks to complete the pattern. In 1893 part of the works was taken over by Messrs G.P. and J. Baker who had at one time the only print works in the country capable of printing on any fabric. The company's hand block printed fabrics gained a wide reputation. G.P. Baker died in 1952 at the age of 95, and 9 years later the works closed.

The other famous works, Messrs David Evans & Company Limited, were originally owned by a Mr Chas Collins. In 1828 Augustus Applegarth came to Crayford and bought out Mr Collins' premises but retained Mr Collins as manager. Augustus Applegarth is perhaps better known for his work in perfecting the printing and numbering of bank notes and other inventions including the 8-cylinder printing press. In the early 1840s Applegarth moved to Dartford to set up

Hand block printing at Crayford. The block is held in the right hand by a pair of holes at the back whilst the left hand accurately guides the block into position. By careful application the printer systematically builds up a pattern.

a new silk printing business and sold the Crayford Works to David and George Evans. Like Charles Swaisland, David Evans was awarded a prize medal at the Great Exhibition for his printed silk handkerchiefs and table covers, and it is interesting to note that under section xviii — 'Miscellaneous fabrics shown as specimens of printing or dyeing' is Mr Charles Swaisland who was recorded as one of the jurors.

For many decades the fabric printers of Crayford produced high class printed fabrics for the wholesale furnishing trade, including printed cretonnes, chintzes, linens, eiderdowns, quilts, cushions, etc., as well as printed silk for the

dress trade. Also produced were the famous Derby silk handkerchiefs, madder handkerchiefs, 'Bandana' handkerchiefs, flags, club stripes and so on.

Favoured woods for the early hand blocks were sycamore, holly and pear which in later days were backed with deal. By the XIXth Century blocks were made using brass or copper strips hammered into the wood. In later days intricate patterns of cast metal were nailed to the wood block. Using fine gas-heated tools a pattern mould was burned out of a solid block of hard wood. Hot alloy was run into the mould which could be knocked out when cold and fixed onto a block.

H.G. Dyer, the village tailor from Minster in Thanet for over half a century.

THE TAILOR

Kent has been known as a premier cloth making county since the Flemish weavers improved the craft many centuries ago. In the XIVth Century Cranbrook was the centre of the weaving industry and Kentish broadcloth was soon to become a well known product. Like many other industries cloth making was a little erratic in success and in the early years of the XVIth Century the industry was going through one of its periods of depression. At this time Kentish clothiers were only allowed to employ new tailors from within the county of Kent to make up the cloth. Failure to comply led to the employer's imprisonment.

Traditionally the craft of the tailor, the art of cutting cloth and fashioning the material to fit a specified shape, has been a man's skill, although in later years often women assisted with the finishing tasks such as buttoning and lining.

Like other craftsmen the tailor had to serve his apprenticeship. He had to learn to sew straight and evenly, so that not only were the stitches at an even distance from each other but they were all the same distance from the cloth edge. In Victorian times the apprentice's first job was often seaming linings for trousers and then learning how to make button holes. The first articles made by the apprentice were vests (waistcoats) which were the easiest. The tailor would then progress through to trouser making and it was often not for many years that the tailor would make a jacket, and that task was often reserved for the best craftsman.

The tailor would usually have to provide his own tools. The most important tools perhaps were scissors, one large pair of cutting shears and a pair of small point scissors for button holes. He would also need chalk, needles and a measure.

Until the First World War most towns had their own tailors, hatters, shoemakers and dressmakers who worked on the premises. Rural folk, especially Kentish farmers, were often reluctant to come into town and so the tailor would go out to his client with his measure book, cloth pattern book and return several times by appointment for fittings.

The great change in the tailor's work came in the mid

An advertisement in an agricultural catalogue of the early 1890s.

Alexander Laing — a tailor from Southborough, Nr Tunbridge Wells working at his treadle sewing machine. The earthenware pot in the fore-ground holds his 'damp rag' for pressing with the iron.

XIXth Century with the general availability of the sewing machine, but even in post Second World War days, especially in the bespoke tailoring trade tailors could occasionally still be seen sitting cross-legged, sewing on a board.

A writer commenting on the craft in 1831 wrote 'Tailors from their confined atmosphere and bad posture are subject to stomach complaints and consumption . . . we see no plump and rosy tailors; none of fine form and strong muscle'.

The illustration shows Alexander Laing a tailor from Southborough near Tunbridge Wells. Mr Laing was with the King's Dragoon Guards in South Africa in 1907 when his family received a communication from the Commander in Chief stating that 'with sympathy and regret' he had to report Laing as a serious casualty as he was dangerously ill with enteric fever. In fact Mr Laing duly recovered and was never ill again in his life and reached the age of 84!

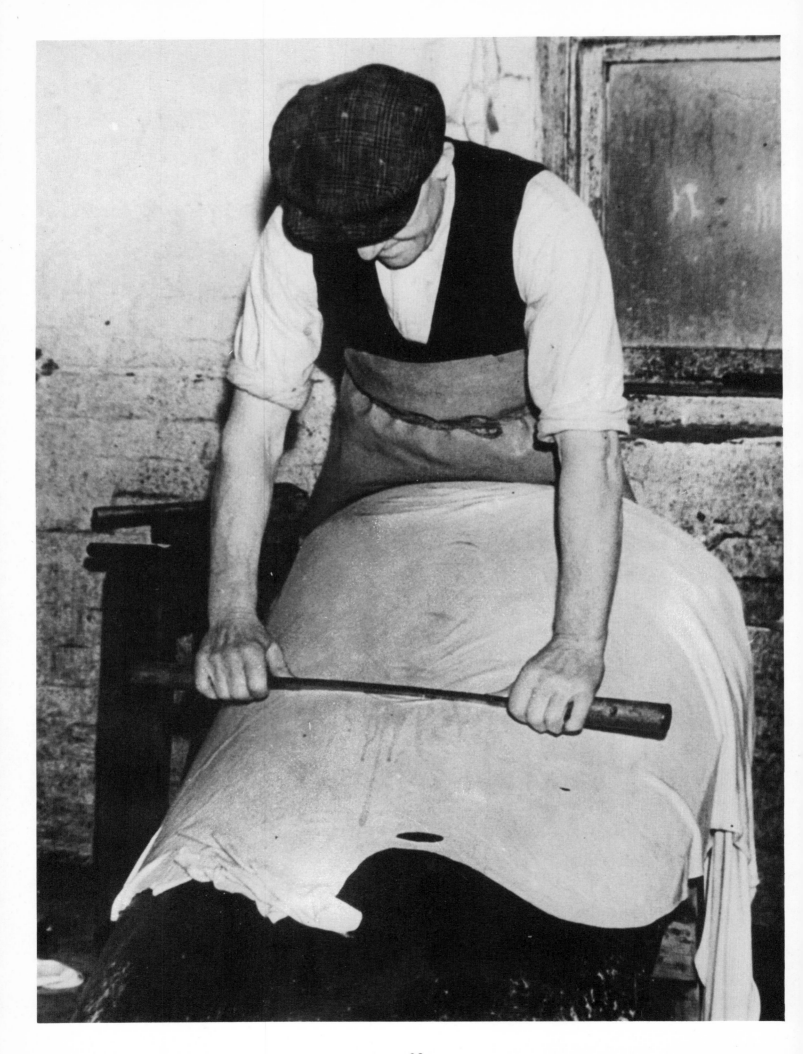

Hand fleshing. After dehairing, the unwanted flesh is skilfully removed with slicing and pushing action of a sharp two handled knife.

THE KENTISH TANNING INDUSTRY

Tanning is the process of converting a perishable skin into virtually non-perishable leather, and perhaps the production of leather is one of the oldest manufacturing industries, as exemplified by Roman and Egyptian finds.

The tanning industry has been established in Kent for many centuries. Certainly the craft of tanning was carried on in Dartford in about 1465 and Hepburn and Company's Priory Works were established in the town in 1852, closed in 1938 and destroyed by fire in 1939. In the 1930s Messrs Whitmore Limited of Edenbridge had been in existence for over three centuries and there were still tanneries at Canterbury, Sandwich, East Peckham, Tenterden, Ashford and Crayford, which at the beginning of the century, employed some 300 people. Today one of the few tanneries still in operation is in Canterbury.

Opposite
Scudding — a process carried out after liming but before tanning to press out broken hairs, follicle remains etc., especially on smooth grain leathers such as calf. The illustration shows Mr Arthur Wood who joined St Mildred's Tannery in 1913 and stayed with the company for 43 years.

The craft of tanning has been an essential industry, for leather is required for a wide number of purposes including boots, clothing, saddlery, book covers, furniture and upholstery. Tanning has been mentioned in various Acts and there were many restrictions imposed. For example, in 1439 tanners were prohibited from being shoemakers; in 1562 butchers were prohibited from becoming tanners under a penalty, and in 1548 an Act was passed which prohibited tanners from selling hides that were not attested to have been in the tan pits for 9 months, although Roberts states in his 'Social History of the Southern Counties of England' that in 1597 there were complaints of leather being so badly dressed that it would not wear satisfactorily when made into shoes.

Many of the restrictions that surrounded leather manufacture remained until 1830 when they were removed under an Act of King George IV. In 1752 tanning was considered to be a 'genteelish business, but owing to the hard labour and being so much in the wet, it required strong and hearty lads to be brought up in it; a journeyman earning 10/- weekly and a master cannot well set up

Dehairing calf skin. After removing the skin from the lime pits, the hairs can be removed by scraping with a blunt two handled curved knife. During the last war, women were employed at St Mildred's Tannery. Initially they were involved on lighter work but they were soon trained to work in the lime pits and tan yards and eventually handled the heavy machinery applicable to sole leather tanning.

in it under a capital of £500' — certainly big money in those days.

Over the past few decades tanneries have been closing in the county, but although in the latter half of the XXth Century there are many leather substitutes, no alternative has yet been found to be totally satisfactory for footwear and saddlery.

Kent had all the essential ingredients for the tanning industry to operate. The Kentish rivers provided the huge quantities of water required and there was also a plentiful supply of oak bark and lime. Furthermore, being an agricultural county, cattle were killed in large numbers to provide the hides. In earlier days before farmers grew winter feed such as swedes and turnips, many animals were killed in the autumn and the meat salted down for the winter months.

Although the method of oak bark tanning is no longer used today it was slow to die out and has certainly been used in post-war days especially for high-class sole leather, cases for surveyor's tapes and other purposes where top quality leather was required. Indeed the sale of oak bark was once a useful by-product of the Kentish forests where oak was commercially grown for charcoal burning and house and ship building. Oak bark is rich in tannins, a

naturally occurring group of chemicals which have the valuable property of arresting the natural decay of skins and hides and converting them into supple, tough and durable leather.

The oak bark obtained from the Weald was always considered to be of a particular high standard and often contained as much as 14% tannin, whilst the oak in parts of the country further north had only about 6% tannin content. Ideally the oaks were barked in the spring for the bark then contained considerably more tannin than that cut in winter, and young oaks yielded more valuable bark than the older trees.

Each tannery was equipped with a bark crusher or mill where the bark was broken down and finely ground and made into a suitable tanning liquid by adding water and allowing the mixture to stand for some weeks before use — rather like making a cup of tea. This process is known as steeping.

The older methods of tanning varied somewhat with each tannery but generally the procedure was to spread the skins out on a block and beat them with a rough mallet to loosen clotted blood and other adhering material. The hair is removed by steeping the hides for several days in a solution of lime liquors of increasing strength, after which they

Another war-time photograph of women working in the tan yard after the bombing in October 1942.

can be satisfactorily dehaired by scraping them on a curved convex bench, known as a beam, with a blunt two-handled curved knife.

After dehairing the skins are 'fleshed' whereby the unwanted tissue on the under or flesh side is cut away. As in dehairing the hide or skin is placed flesh side up on the beam, but unlike dehairing a sharp double-handled knife is used with a slicing and pushing action. Fleshing is a highly skilled process for the hides can be so easily damaged by careless cutting.

Nothing is wasted in the tanning industry and the excess flesh can be used for making furniture glue and size and is also sold to the gelatine industry for food processing and to the photographic and paper industry.

Often the hides have to be split. Cattle hide is usually some 4.5mm thick and before the splitting machine was introduced the hides were shaved after tanning with a double edged tool known as a currier's knife. Shaving was also essential because natural skin varies in thickness. The neck of calf skins can be twice as thick as the remainder. Today the hides are split into two or more layers by precision machines rather like a bacon-slicing machine operating in a horizontal direction. The top split is of prime quality insomuch as it carries the 'grain layer'.

After washing and deliming the pelts, as the hides and skins are called at this stage, are ready to be tanned. They are placed in pits containing the tanning solution and over a period the skins are passed through a progression of pits usually arranged in shifts, each shift usually containing 8 pits.

The first pit holds a weak solution and pelts progress through the pits finishing with a strong solution. With oak bark tanning this process could take the best part of a year.

When the process of tanning is complete, the butts are slowly and completely dried. In the last century, in the preparation of heavy brown harness leather, linseed oil was rubbed into the hide after drying and the skin beaten until the desired colour was obtained. To heighten the lustre, sweetened milk or ideally a solution of crocus is rubbed over. Heavy skins to be used for blacksmiths' aprons, furnace workers, etc. were also tawed in alum and salt after bark treatment.

Today there are many different tanning materials and large revolving drums have replaced the pits. The drum keeps the hides in constant motion and the tanning period has been reduced to a matter of days rather than months or even years when oak bark was used.

Hides hanging up to dry naturally in the drying loft.

One of the last remaining tanneries in Kent is the old established firm of Messrs J.J. Williamson & Sons (Canterbury) Limited of St Mildred's Tannery. The firm goes back to 1791 when it occupied a site on the corner of Sun Street and Guildhall Street, Canterbury, and is run by the 8th generation of the Williamson family. Like many other tanneries in the county the firm provided agricultural leather, army leather, sole leather, harness and saddle leather and so on, and in the early 1900s with the introduction of the motor vehicle the firm went over to car upholstery leather. For nearly half a century the production of upholstery leather and sole leather went on together, but in the 1950s the demand for heavy leather and high quality sole leather diminished. The company now processes several thousand hides a week and specialises in making top grade upholstery leather and bridle leather.

St Mildred's Tannery has been providing the leather for Rolls Royce since before the First World War and also supplies many other prestige motor companies with car upholstery. The firm also supplies the leather for such specialised work as desk-tops, furniture, clothing and seats for Houses of Parliament all over the world including our own House of Commons.

In recent years Williamson's hides have come mainly from Europe, especially Scandinavia where the best hides, free from grain faults, are to be found. However in the 1980s English hides are being used again. Some years ago English hides were too much spoilt by warble fly attack but due to recent legislation as to the dressing of cattle, the hides have greatly improved.

St Mildred's Tannery is now the largest upholstery leather tanners in the Common Market and is the only traditional manufacturing industry still operating within the ancient city walls. Today most of the procedures described above are out of date and many of the processes are carried out mechanically with sophisticated automatic and computer techniques.

Richard Sharvill of Boyce, Brown & Kemp at work at the Camden Road workshop, Tunbridge Wells.

An excellent example of turned Tonbridge ware from the Tunbridge Wells Museum collection.

TUNBRIDGE WARE

Craftsmen in the Tonbridge and Tunbridge Wells area have been producing decorated wooden articles known as Tunbridge Ware from the XVIIth Century until the XXth Century. The actual year the first Tunbridge Ware was introduced is unknown but one claim is that the industry was first established in 1629. Certainly the availability of wood in the area had attracted wood turners quite early on and when Lord North discovered the Chalybeate Springs in 1606 no doubt the wood craftsmen produced mementoes to sell to the Spa visitors. The diarist Celia Fiennes recorded in 1697 that at Tunbridge Wells there were 'shopps full of toys . . . and all sorts of curios, wooden ware, which this place is noted . . . the delicate neat and thin ware of wood both white and lignum vitae wood'.

One of the early families producing the ware were George Wise and his decendants whose workshop was in Tonbridge and later in Tunbridge Wells in the XIXth Century. The Jordan manufactory was at Jordan Place from about 1685 to 1740 and the building still stands today. Burrows started producing at a workshop at Speldhurst in about 1720 and the four Burrows brothers who improved the technique later on, were producing most exquisite work from about 1820 to about 1845.

Perhaps the heyday of Tunbridge Ware manufacture was the second half of the XIXth Century. The most famous craftsmen producing the ware of this period include Edmond Nye, Robert Russell, who invented Tunbridge Wells marquetry, Henry Hollamby and Thomas Barton,

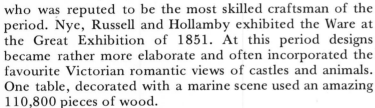

Richard Sharvill selecting strips to make up a block. His firm did not close until 1927.

Tea caddy with perspective cube design made at the Wise manufactory.

who was reputed to be the most skilled craftsman of the period. Nye, Russell and Hollamby exhibited the Ware at the Great Exhibition of 1851. At this period designs became rather more elaborate and often incorporated the favourite Victorian romantic views of castles and animals. One table, decorated with a marine scene used an amazing 110,800 pieces of wood.

Much of the wood used was readily available locally such as holly, cherry, plum, yew and of course sycamore, the favourite wood of the turners, but as 180 or so different woods were used to obtain the extremely wide range of shades from black through the browns to white, some of the woods were imported. The true Tunbridge Ware was never dyed and a much prized wood was oak that had been affected by a fungus which gave it a positive green tint. Some of the wood was soaked in water from the Chalybeate Springs which also had the effect of altering the colours a little.

Although the Tunbridge Ware manufacture called for most accurate cutting, the tools used were relatively simple. Wafers of wood usually measuring about 6″ x 1″ with a thickness of only 1/6th″ were carefully prepared. The 'bandsman' would glue and clamp together a quantity of selected pieces to form a block. When set, 1/16th″ strips could be sliced off the block by cutting across the cross-grain of the original slips and creating a striped slip. These could then be glued together in such a way to form a 'chequerboard' section. The slices could then be cut horizontally from the block creating a considerable quantity of patterned veneer.

The products produced by the Tunbridge Ware craftsman tended to change with the fashion of the day. The range was most extensive and virtually any commodity that possibly have the excuse for a Tunbridge Ware design was offered to visitors. Boxes of all sorts of shapes and sizes were produced. There were glove boxes, games boxes, cribbage boxes, handkerchief boxes, match boxes, snuff boxes and so on, there were cases for tape measures and cases for needles. There were brushes for hair, brushes for coats, there were puzzles, pen holders, picture frames, tea caddies, worktables, ring holders, rulers, perfume bottle stands and chess tables; together with napkin rings, book markers, sewing clamps, silk skein holders, knitting needle protectors, ladles, darning eggs, thread spools and perhaps most surprising of all a seven-string banjo. No member of the Spa visitor's family could escape the traditional present from Tunbridge Wells.

Although perhaps the artistic merit of many of the pieces is questionable, for imagination and sound and accurate craftsmanship in wood, the work is outstanding.

By the end of the XIXth Century the only company left producing the ware was the old firm of Boyce, Brown and Kemp which was wound up in 1927. Mr Kemp Junior attempted to revive the craft in Rye in 1932 but the premises were destroyed during the war. It is perhaps surprising that with the current interest in handcrafts that in 1982 no fresh attempt has been made to start production again.

THE UPHOLSTERER

The craft of the upholsterer is perhaps older than might be expected. The trade is thought to have evolved from the ancient skill of tent-making, and when the Upholsterers' Company, one of the oldest of the City of London guilds and livery companies was granted a coat of arms it consisted of a shield with three tent beds emblazoned in 1465.

Upholstery is a trade allied to that of the cabinet-maker and it was the upholsterer who carried out what is known as the 'soft work', i.e. undertaking the curtains, cushions, beds and the stuffing of chairs and so on. It is the upholsterer's task to make the finished piece of furniture pleasant to look at and, perhaps more important, comfortable to sit on. The early upholsterers were known as 'upholders' and this term persisted through to the XIXth Century.

The first attempt in England to make chairs more comfortable was to stretch strips of leather across the seats. During the XIVth Century some chairs were made with a cushioned seat, but it was not until late Elizabethan times that the insertion of stuffing between the material and the frame became common, but materials were expensive. Inventories for the end of the XVIth Century revealed that velvet cost between 15/- and 30/- per yard, which was a huge sum in those days.

A taste for luxury spread and perhaps the upholsterer's craft reached its heyday in the reign of James I when the level of luxury and comfort remained unsurpassed even by the late Victorian and early Edwardian upholsterers with the new taste for the plush deep buttoned work in velvets, damasks and moroccos.

After the First World War, with the availability of utilitarian factory-made furniture, the craft of the upholsterer, or 'ragtacker' as he was often referred to in the furniture trade, began to dwindle. A Kent directory for 1895 lists 132 upholstery firms which declined rapidly until in the 1960s there were only a handful of upholsterers left in the county. In the 1980s there are several traditional upholsterers' workshops in Kent and with a renewed interest in period furniture the upholsterer's craft is in great demand again and several young men have learnt the skill and opened their own workshops. However, the majority of the upholsterer's time is now taken up with restoring antique furniture.

Perhaps the finest collection of early upholstered furniture in the country can be viewed at Knole House, Sevenoaks.

With period furniture gaining popularity the skills of the upholsterer are much sought after.

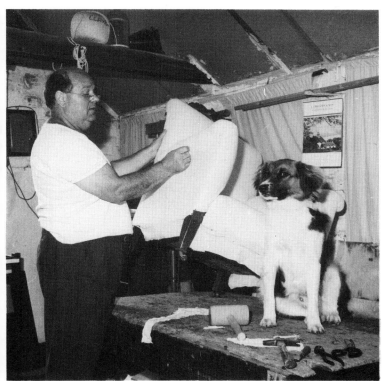

A Deal upholsterer.

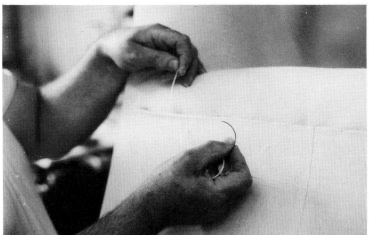

Note the curved upholsterers needle.

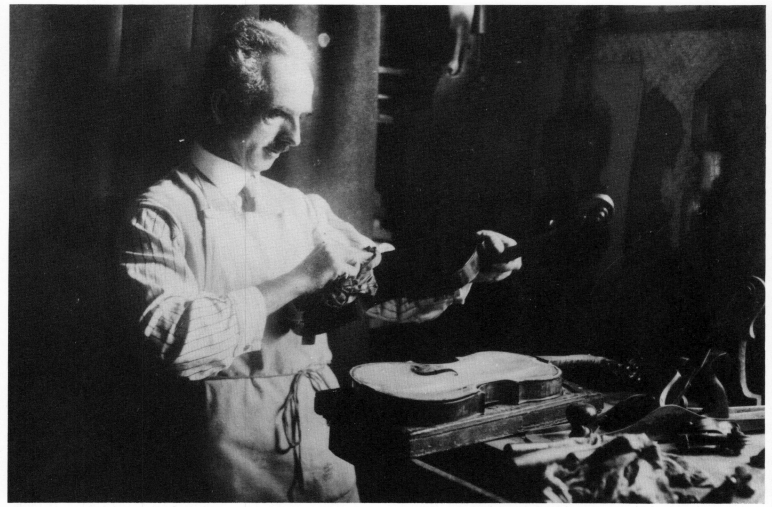
Alfred Dixon who lived at Cheriton, Nr Folkestone, polishing the back of a violin.

THE VIOLIN MAKER

The ancestry of the violin is rather complex, the forerunners being instruments such as the fydel, rebec and the lyra da Braccio. A XIIth Century rebec is portrayed in the crypt at Canterbury Cathedral and a rybybe of the same period is depicted at the church of St Nicholas, Barfrestone, near Dover. However, the earliest representation of the violin as we know it today, is illustrated on a fresco in Saroma Cathedral in Italy dating from around 1535. Obviously the instrument used by Nero who 'fiddled while Rome burned' and Old King Cole who possibly reigned in Britain in about the IIIrd Century AD and 'called for his fiddlers three', are references to forms of these earlier instruments and not that natural and seemingly ageless shape that we know today.

The origin of the word 'fiddle' is lost in obscurity. Fyddelles are mentioned in old translations of the Bible and today most violin makers use the word affectionately, often preferring the word to violin.

The violin follows the same basic principle of all stringed instruments in that a length of string, wire or gut is held in tension between two points and when vibrated a note is emitted and amplified by the box. When the string is shortened a higher note is obtained.

Perhaps the English violin makers have never gained the status of the great Italian masters, although the father of Galileo, the famous astronomer said in 1583 that the English made the best lutes in the world. The lack of status of the English makers was possibly because they copied the Stainer model which was to lose popularity to the Stradivari model. However, there have been some notable makers over the centuries and always a healthy supply of native built instruments.

In 1750 Barek Norman, originally a viol maker, was making fiddles in St Paul's Churchyard and later in the XVIIIth Century the famous Hill family began building instruments. At this time other famous English makers included William Forster, the son of a spinning-wheel maker, and Benjamin Banks who pioneered the revival of the Cremonese models. In more recent times there have been several notable makers in Kent especially in the Folkestone and Dover areas such as the prolific George Buckman born in 1825 who lived at Kearsney, near Dover, and George St George whose violins can be recognised by the inlaid cross of St George on the back of the instrument. Alfred Chanot who died in 1957 lived in Folkestone and Alfred Dixon who used to live in a house named 'Cremona' in Cheriton, near Folkestone, was well known throughout Kent and Sussex in the early decades of this century. In the 1980s Bill Laing of Lyminge is making instruments of outstanding workmanship, both in modern and baroque form, whilst Jack Tompsett of Folkestone also makes instruments of superb tonal quality.

Bill Laing thicknessing the belly of a violin.

Using a profile to check the curvature which has a significant effect on the tone and power of a complete instrument.

Bill Laing using a tiny thumb plane for shaping. Some of the tools used in this violin maker's workshop belonged to Henry Fuller (born 1863) who continued making instruments when he retired to Dover. Mr Fuller also made small violins which were popular with ladies.

The construction of this perfectly proportioned instrument from a few ounces of wood is an exercise of patience, skill and thorough understanding of every millimetre of wood used. Certainly these qualities are far more important than a well equipped and elaborate workshop. The instrument is made up of about 85 separate pieces, all, with the exception of the scroll, being entirely functional and shaped

the way it is for a positive reason. The belly (front) of the body is carefully selected straight fibred spruce usually Swiss and ideally from a slow grown tree with a minimum of 12 annual rings to the inch and absolutely knot free. The back traditionally is of sycamore or maple. Sycamore is usually straight grained but European sycamore has wavy grain much sought after by the makers and is felled after

Using a reamer to enlarge and taper the holes in the peg box of a violin.

Carefully shaping the violin back. The thicknesses of the back and belly varies in different parts from 1/16th to 3/16th of an inch.

50 to 100 years growth. It is the selection of the wood that can enhance the mellow, warm and powerful tone of the completed instrument. Some of the early makers even insisted upon the wood coming from the south side of the tree and furthermore insisted that the tree should be felled in December or January.

Like the woodland craftsmen the violin maker ideally cleaves the wood along the grain and insists that the wood must be naturally seasoned, for no maker would consider using kiln dried material.

Upon close examination of a violin body the shape is rather more complex than seen at first glance. The lower part is wider than the upper and the waist which gives the bow some freedom is indented in the form of a 'C' on either side. The middle is arched and flattens out to a bevel near the edge, and obviously both the back and the belly must correspond acoustically with each other.

Many people feel that the back and belly are somehow pressed into shape out of a thin piece of wood but this is most definitely not the case, for the back and the belly are skilfully shaped with saws and gauges and minutely finished with tiny thumb planes and scrapers from a solid block of wood. The shape and form of the arched belly has great influence on the tone so the work must proceed slowly and with much caution, for once even the thinnest extra shaving has been removed it cannot be replaced and the tone can be so easily ruined. The thickness varies in different parts from 1/16th" to 3/16th". A high curvature softens the tone whilst the lower curvature will increase the power.

The almost eggshell thinness of the body is essential to obtain the most resonant box and the body must also be

A groove is marked from the edge with a purfling tool and deepened by hand with a gouge. Strips of wood known as 'the purfling' are inlaid.

light enough to be held by the chin alone when playing but coupled with this, it must be enormously strong to withstand the tremendous tension on the strings.

The head and neck which must be so accurately fitted to the body are hand carved from sycamore and when the violin has been completely constructed 'in the white' it must be oiled or spirit varnished.